Wolfgang Amadeus Mozart

Violin Concerto No. 4 in D major / D-Dur
K 218

Edited by / Herausgegeben von
Richard Clarke

T0081239

EULENBURG

EAS 198
ISBN 978-3-7957-6598-9
ISMN 979-0-2002-2629-4

© 2016 Ernst Eulenburg & Co GmbH, Mainz
for Europe excluding the British Isles
Ernst Eulenburg Ltd, London
for all other countries
CD ℗ 1999 NAXOS Rights US, Inc.
CD © 2016 Ernst Eulenburg Ltd, London

Ernst Eulenburg Ltd
48 Great Marlborough Street
London W1F 7BB

Contents / Inhalt

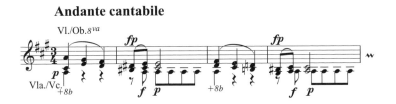

III. Rondeau. Andante grazioso –
Allegro ma non troppo

Andante grazioso

Allegro ma non troppo

Preface

Composed: October 1775 in Salzburg
First performance: unknown
Original publisher: first edition (posthumously) in 1807 by
André, Offenbach
Instrumentation: 2 Oboes – 2 Horns – Strings
Duration: ca. 20 minutes

The Salzburg years between 1773 and summer 1777 belong amongst the happiest, more or less carefree periods of Mozart's brief life. Aside from stays in Vienna and Munich, it was a time without exhausting concert tours, without pressing, often even ignominious, self-promotion and still largely devoid of friction with his employer Hieronymus Count Colloredo (1732–1812), prince-archbishop of Salzburg, or the estrangement from his father Leopold (1719–1787) that first appeared evermore besetting from the fall of 1776. As a 19-year-old in 1775, he had indeed long since outgrown his period as child-prodigy, but whilst under the protection of his parental home, still did not have to cope with the problems of daily life. Mozart rendered his musical services to Colloredo, carried out orders for church and court concerts and, as appreciated and acknowledged composer, also most notably wrote instrumental music of an entertaining character – serenades, 'night music', 'finale music', cassations or divertimentos – for the Salzburg nobility and affluent urban bourgeoisie. This was 'casual music' that through its hardly ever again attained musical quality admittedly put very much in the shade the often-coincidental occasions of its origin (such as weddings, anniversaries, name- or birthdays) with particular specifications even extending to the music's scoring. Mozart did not by any means feel such specifications as constraints and regimentation of his musical art of invention, rather they stimulated and challenged him and unleashed his creativity. He advanced, as Alfred Orel put it, from being the son of the respected vice-capellmeister Leopold to the 'cavaliere servente' [i.e., gallant] of Salzburg society. It was even felt that from these works could be inferred Mozart's confident, powerfully positive attitude towards life in those times.

Mozart doubtless also established his reputation as a brilliant pianist, but as pupil of his father who had published in 1756 an important textbook in his *Versuch einer gründlichen Violinschule*, he was also a first-rate violinist who was heard and achieved signal success in public. 'You have no idea how well you play violin', his father wrote him; and Mozart even let his father know that in his violin playing on 4 October 1777 in Munich he had played 'as if I were the greatest violinist in Europe'. Concerning a concert that he gave on 19 October 1777 in Augsburg at which, besides his own third violin concerto in G major K216, he also played a violin concerto by Johann Baptist Vanhall, he reported: 'It went like oil, everyone praised the beautiful, pure tone.'

Mozart certainly played not so much with sophisticated virtuosity as instead with clarity, poise and logic – judging by the criteria with which he himself extolled the playing of other musicians. Yet already in 1778 he shelved violin playing entirely and wrote his father, for instance, on 11 September 1778: 'I ask for only one thing in Salzburg, and that is: that I am not at the violin as I once was – I'm no longer a violinist; I want to conduct and accompany arias at the piano.'

But Mozart composed violin concertos only at the time when he himself was active as violinist. After the first violin concerto in B flat major K207 of April 1773 – his very first independent concerto altogether – Mozart immediately produced four other concertos (No.2 in D major K211; No.3 in G major K216; No.4 in D major K218 and No.5 in A major K219) in Salzburg between June and December 1775; these evidently were initially for his own performance, though soon afterwards they were then performed by friends such as the violinist Johann Anton Kolb or the Salzburg court concertmaster Antonio Brunetti. In several of Mozart's serenades there are also of course not only concertante movements for violin and orchestra (K185, for example), but also sets of sequential movements that could attain the dimensions of three-movement violin concertos (K250, for example). These performances occurred less often in concert halls than in gardens, in piazzas, as intermezzos at opera performances or in churches. The fourth concerto in D major K218 originated in October 1775; on the title-page Leopold Mozart wrote: 'Concerto per | il Vionlino | del Sgr Cavaliere Amadeo | Wolfgango Mozart | nel octobre 1775 à Salisburgo'. The work's autograph score, presently preserved as part of a bundle of concertos K207, K211 and K216 in the Biblioteka Jagiellońska Kraków (formerly: Prussian State Library), organises the parts differently from that to which we are accustomed: notated at the top is the solo violin, followed by violins I and II, viola, 2 oboes, 2 horns and the bass. In the Salzburg orchestral scoring of the period the first and second violins were scored for 6 to 7 players, the violas for 2 players, whereas the bass was played by a cello, 2 doublebasses and sometimes 1 to 2 bassoons. Conspicuous corrections in the autograph are to be found only in movements II and III: after bar 80 in movement II Mozart replaced a five-bar first version with 10 new bars giving the soloist an opportunity after bar 85 to play a cadenza-like transition; after bar 208 in movement III, he wrote a new transition to the last *Andante grazioso* section. Mozart marked dynamics in the solo part very sparingly – quite in the style of the period – and did not even write down any kind of cadenza. Only in 1807 was the first edition of this concerto published, as 'Op.121' in a set of parts by Johann Anton André in Offenbach – 16 years after Mozart's death.

In his violin concertos Mozart followed the Vivaldi three-movement concerto form and in the first movements the conventional four tutti sections (introduction, beginning of development, transition to the cadenza, coda) and three solo sections (exposition, development and re-capitulation, cadenza). But he gave the music a completely different characteristic style in which perceptibly remaining and valued as the epitome and complete expression of musical *galanterie* (Erich Schenk) were influences of the Mannheim symphony, the opera-buffa melody, influences of Johann Christian Bach or of French and Italian violin music written by such as Giovanni Battista Viotti (1755–1824) or Pietro Nardini (1722–1793). For a long time it was assumed that in his fourth violin concerto K218 Mozart had followed a D major violin concerto by Boccherini, though in the meantime this Boccherini violin concerto has proved to be a forgery, itself taking as its model Mozart's K218.

The four violin concertos composed in 1775 do indeed possess a unified and directly comparable structure, yet Mozart has given each of these concertos an unmistakeable character and in them immensely refined and differentiated the concerto form without being repetitive. In keeping with the times, Mozart takes the solo part of the fourth violin concerto K218 into an unusually high register – it ranges up to an a³, even to a d⁴ in bar 120 of the final movement – and writes for it really virtuosic passage work, yet nowhere is this obtrusive; it ever remains integrated in an exceptionally tight network of thematic connections. The orchestral tutti of the introduction to the first movement brings in no fewer than seven thematic configurations that Mozart put together in the subsequent exposition entirely for the purpose of the two conventional sections of the main-theme group (bb42–86) and subsidiary-theme group (bb86–109), but augmented as well with a new theme (bb57ff.) that proves to be extremely significant: with this theme – and not with the main theme as such – Mozart can begin the recapitulation (b145), even omitting the main theme altogether. Movement II, whose tempo marking *Andante cantabile*, incidentally, Leopold Mozart entered into the score, brings to mind the considerable formal influence of the aria on the Mozart concerto form. It can be understood as a movement in (first-movement) sonata form that is lacking however a development section. The exposition with the three theme groups, main theme (bb1–21) in the tonic key of A major, subsidiary theme (bb21–30), together with the closing group (bb30–39) in the dominant E major, and a closing phrase returning from the dominant back to the tonic key (bb39–42), is repeated entirely in order to recapitulate the harmonic-tonal relationship in the tonic key. Thus, in this recapitulation Mozart also harmonically turns the extraordinarily continuous, uninterrupted 'song' of the solo violin inside out. The closing 'Rondeau' with its lucid sequential form also possesses definite 'French' traits in its characteristic music style. Here, lavishly and with sophistication, Mozart thematically develops the couplet parts articulated by the recurring refrain subject. In the middle couplet (bb126–178) he even uses folk music and also adds a *bourdon* in bb136ff., giving the music a musette-like character. For a long time this allusion was identified as a 'Strassburg' melody that Mozart and his father also mention in letters, without actually naming the work itself. Meanwhile, however, Dénes Bartha has shown that 'Strassburg' refers to the analogous section in the final movement of the third violin concerto K216, which quotes a song headed: 'An obscure lied, *ad notam Strassburger*', from an Hungarian song collection.

Giselher Schubert
Translation: Margit L. McCorkle

Vorwort

Komponiert: Oktober 1775 in Salzburg
Uraufführung: unbekannt
Originalverlag: zu Lebzeiten des Komponisten nicht gedruckt
Erstausgabe André, Offenbach 1807
Orchesterbesetzung: 2 Oboen – 2 Hörner – Streicher
Spieldauer: ca. 20 Minuten

Die Salzburger Jahre zwischen 1773 und Sommer 1777 zählen zur glücklichsten, einigermaßen unbeschwerten Zeit in Mozarts kurzem Leben. Abgesehen von Aufenthalten in Wien und München war es eine Zeit ohne strapaziöse Konzertreisen, ohne andienender, oft dann auch entwürdigender Eigenwerbung und noch weitgehend ohne die Spannungen zu seinem Dienstherrn Hieronymus Graf Colloredo (1732–1812), Fürstbischhof zu Salzburg, oder die Entfremdung von seinem Vater Leopold (1719–1787), die sich erst seit Herbst 1776 immer bedrängender einstellten. 1775, als 19-Jähriger, war er wohl seiner Wunderkind-Zeit längst entwachsen, aber er hatte in der Obhut seines Elternhauses noch nicht mit den alltäglichen Lebensproblemen zu kämpfen. Mozart leistete für Colloredo seinen Kapelldienst, führte die Aufträge für Kirchen- und Hofkonzerte aus und schrieb als geschätzter und anerkannter Komponist vor allem auch Instrumentalmusiken unterhaltenden Charakters – Serenaden, „Nachtmusiken", „Finalmusiken", Kassationen oder Divertimenti – für den Salzburger Adel und das wohlhabende Bürgertum der Stadt. Das waren „Gelegenheitsmusiken", die freilich die oft zufälligen Anlässe ihrer Entstehung (etwa Hochzeiten, Jubiläen, Namens- oder Geburtstage) mit besonderen, bis in die Besetzung der Musik hineinreichenden Vorgaben durch ihre kaum jemals wieder erreichte musikalische Qualität weit hinter sich ließen. Mozart empfand solche Vorgaben keinesfalls als Einschränkung und Reglementierung seiner musikalischen Erfindungskunst, sondern sie stimulierten ihn, forderten ihn heraus und entfesselten seine Kreativität. Mozart rückte, wie Alfred Orel es ausdrückte, vom Sohn des geachteten Vizekapellmeisters Leopold zum „Cavaliere servante" der Salzburger Gesellschaft auf. Man glaubte sogar, aus diesen Werken auf ein zuversichtliches, kraftvoll-positives Lebensgefühl Mozarts in jener Zeit schließen zu können.

Mozart machte sich wohl auch als glänzender Pianist einen Namen, aber er war als Schüler seines Vaters, der 1756 mit seinem *Versuch einer gründlichen Violinschule* ein bedeutendes Lehrwerk veröffentlicht hatte, auch ein vorzüglicher Geiger, der sich öffentlich hören ließ und beachtliche Erfolge erzielte. „Du weißt selbst nicht, wie gut Du Violin spielst", schrieb ihm der Vater, und Mozart selbst meldete dem Vater über sein Geigenspiel am 4. Oktober 1777 in München, er habe gespielt „als wenn ich der gröste geiger in Europa wäre". Über ein Konzert, das er am 19. Oktober 1777 in Augsburg gab und bei dem er neben seinem 3. Violinkonzert G-Dur KV 216 auch ein Violinkonzert von Johann Baptist Vanhall spielte, berichtete er ihm: „Es gieng wie öhl, alles lobte den schönen, reinen Ton." Mozart spielte freilich weniger mit aufwändiger Virtuosität, als vielmehr – geurteilt nach den Kriterien, mit denen er selbst das Spiel anderer Musiker rühmte – mit musikalischer Klarheit, Ausgeglichenheit und Logik. Doch bereits 1778 stellte er das Geigenspiel gänzlich zurück und schrieb etwa am 11. September 1778 dem Vater: „Nur eins bitte ich mir zu salzburg aus, und das ist: das ich nicht bey der violin bin, wie ich sonst war – keinen Geiger gebe ich nicht mehr ab; beym clavier will ich dirigirn die arien accompagnieren."

Violinkonzerte komponierte Mozart denn auch nur zu der Zeit, zu der er selbst als Geiger aktiv war. Nach dem 1. Violinkonzert B-Dur, KV 207, vom April 1773 – das war sein erstes eigenständiges Konzertwerk überhaupt – fertigte er gleich vier weitere Konzerte (Nr. 2 D-Dur, KV 211; Nr. 3 G-Dur, KV 216; Nr. 4 D-Dur, KV 218 und Nr. 5 A-Dur, KV 219) zwischen Juni und Dezember 1775 in Salzburg an: offensichtlich zunächst für den eigenen Vortrag, doch wurden sie dann alsbald etwa von Freunden wie dem Geiger Johann Anton Kolb oder dem Salzburger Hofkonzertmeister Antonio Brunetti aufgeführt. Freilich finden sich auch in einigen der Serenaden Mozarts nicht nur konzertante Sätze für Violine und Orchester (zum Beispiel KV 185), sondern auch Satzfolgen, welche die Dimensionen von dreisätzigen Violin-konzerten (zum Beispiel KV 250) gewinnen können. Diese Aufführungen fanden weniger in Konzertsälen statt, sondern in Gärten, auf Plätzen, als Zwischenaktmusiken bei Opernauf-führungen oder in Kirchen. Das 4. Konzert D-Dur, KV 218, entstand im Oktober 1775; auf die Titelseite schrieb Leopold Mozart: „Concerto per | il Vionlino | del Sgr Cavaliere Amadeo | Wolfgango Mozart | nel octobre 1775 à Salisburgo". Die autografe Partitur des Werkes, die gegenwärtig als Teil eines Konvoluts mit den Konzerten KV 207, KV 211 und KV 216 in der Biblioteka Jagiellońska Kraków (früher: Preußische Staatsbibliothek) aufbewahrt wird, ordnet die Stimmen anders an, als wir es gewohnt sind: An der obersten Stelle ist die Solovioline notiert, auf die Violine I und II, Bratsche, 2 Oboen, 2 Hörner und der Bass folgen. In den Salzburger Orchesterbesetzungen der Zeit wurden die ersten und zweiten Violinen mit 6 bis 7 Spielern besetzt, die Bratschen mit 2 Spielern, während der Bass von einem Cello, 2 Kontra-bässen und mitunter 1 bis 2 Fagotten gespielt wurde. Auffällige Korrekturen finden sich in Mozarts Partitur nur im II. und III. Satz: Im II. Satz ersetzte Mozart nach T. 80 eine fünf-taktige Erstfassung durch zehn neue Takte, mit denen nach Takt 85 der Solist Gelegenheit erhält, kadenzartig eine Überleitung zu spielen; im III. Satz schrieb er nach Takt 208 eine neue Überleitung zum letzten Andante grazioso-Abschnitt. Mozart hat – ganz im Stile der Zeit – die Solostimme dynamisch äußerst spärlich bezeichnet und selbst auch keine Kadenzen niedergeschrieben. Ein Erstdruck der Stimmen dieses Konzertes erschien erst 1807 bei Johann Anton André in Offenbach als „op. 121" – 16 Jahre nach Mozarts Tod.

Mozart schloss in seinen Violinkonzerten wohl noch an die dreisätzige Konzertform Vivaldis oder etwa an die konventionellen vier Tutti- (Einleitung, Durchführungsbeginn, Hinleitung zur Kadenz, Coda) und drei Soloteile (Exposition, Durchführung und Reprise, Kadenz) im Kopfsatz an, gab aber der Musik einen völlig veränderten Duktus, in dem Einflüsse der Mannheimer Sinfonik, der Melodik aus der Opera buffa, Einflüsse von Johann Christian Bach oder von französischer und italienischer Violinmusik, wie sie etwa Giovanni Battista Viotti

(1755–1824) oder Pietro Nardini (1722–1793) schrieben, spürbar blieben und die als Inbegriff und vollendeter Ausdruck musikalischer Galanterie (Erich Schenk) eingeschätzt wurden. Eine Zeit lang nahm man auch an, Mozart wäre im 4. Violinkonzert, KV 218, unmittelbar einem D-Dur Violinkonzert von Boccherini gefolgt, doch hat sich mittlerweile dieses Violinkonzert von Boccherini als das Werk eines Fälschers erwiesen, der sich Mozarts KV 218 zum Vorbild genommen hatte.

Die vier 1775 komponierten Violinkonzerte besitzen wohl eine einheitliche und unmittelbar vergleichbare Faktur, doch hat Mozart jedem dieser Konzerte einen unverwechselbaren Charakter gegeben und mit ihnen die Konzertform ungemein verfeinert und differenziert, ohne sich zu wiederholen. Die Solostimme des 4. Violinkonzertes, KV 218, führt Mozart, einem Zug der Zeit folgend, ungewöhnlich hoch – sie reicht bis zum a^3, im Finalsatz findet sich sogar in Takt 210 ein d^4 – und schreibt ihr durchaus virtuoses Passagenwerk vor, doch nirgendwo wirkt es aufdringlich; stets bleibt es in ein ungemein dicht geknüpftes Netz thematischer Bezüge eingebunden. Das Orchestertutti der Einleitung zum I. Satz führt nicht weniger als 7 thematische Konfigurationen ein, die Mozart im folgenden Expositionsteil ganz im Sinne der beiden konventionellen Abschnitte von Hauptthemengruppe (Takt 42–86) und Seitenthemengruppe (Takt 86–109) zusammenfügt, aber auch noch mit einem neuen Thema ergänzt (Takt 57ff.), das sich als äußerst bedeutend erweist: Mit diesem Thema – und nicht etwa mit dem Hauptthema – lässt Mozart die Reprise (Takt 145) einsetzen, welche das Hauptthema sogar gänzlich ausspart. Der II. Satz, dessen Tempovorschrift „Andante cantabile" übrigens Leopold Mozart in die Partitur eintrug, vergegenwärtigt den beträchtlichen Einfluss der Arienform auf die mozartsche Konzertform. Er lässt sich als ein Satz in der Sonatenhauptsatzform auffassen, der freilich ein Durchführungsabschnitt fehlt. Der Expositionsteil mit den drei Themengruppen von Hauptthema (Takt 1–21) in der Grundtonart A-Dur, Seitenthema (Takt 21–30) sowie Schlussgruppe (Takt 30–39) auf der Dominante E-Dur und einer von der Dominante zur Grundtonart zurückleitenden Schlusswendung (Takt 39–42) wird ganz im Sinne der harmonisch-tonalen Verhältnisse einer Reprise in der Grundtonart wiederholt. Dadurch kehrt Mozart den ungemein kontinuierlichen, durchlaufenden „Gesang" der Solovioline in dieser Reprise auch harmonisch nach außen. Das abschließende „Rondeau" mit seiner übersichtlichen Reihungsform besitzt auch im Duktus der Musik durchaus „französische" Züge. Hier gestaltet Mozart die vom wiederkehrenden Refrain-Thema gegliederten Couplet-Teile thematisch verschwenderisch reich und differenziert aus. Im mittleren Couplet (Takt 126–178) lässt er sogar Volksmusik anklingen und fügt Takt 136ff. auch einen Bordun hinzu, welcher der Musik einen Musette-Charakter gibt. Diese Anspielung wurde eine Zeit lang als Melodie des „Straßburger" identifiziert, die Mozart und auch sein Vater in Briefen erwähnen, ohne freilich das Werk zu benennen, das sie meinen. Mittlerweile konnte jedoch Dénes Bartha zeigen, dass mit „Straßburger" der analog gestaltete Abschnitt im Finalsatz des 3. Violinkonzertes, KV 216, gemeint ist, der ein Lied aus einer ungarischen Liedersammlung zitiert, das die Überschrift trägt: „Ein unverständliches Lied, ad notam Straßburger".

Giselher Schubert

Violin Concerto No. 4

Wolfgang Amadeus Mozart
(1756–1791)
K 218

EAS 198

Edited by Richard Clarke
© 2016 Ernst Eulenburg Ltd, London
and Ernst Eulenburg & Co GmbH, Mainz

4

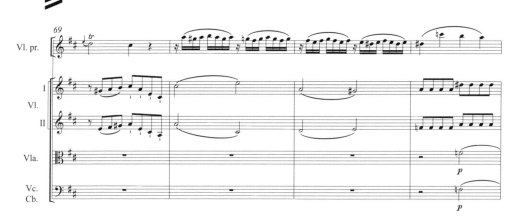

12

14

16

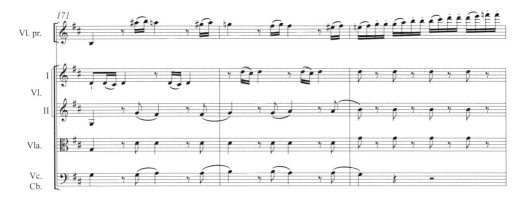

22

*) Cadenza

24

II. Andante cantabile

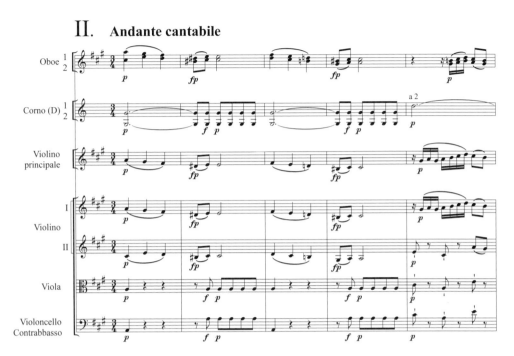

SOLO

28

30

34

III. RONDEAU

Andante grazioso

Allegro ma non troppo

36

EAS 198

38

Allegro ma non troppo

42

Andante grazioso

44

Andante grazioso

Allegro ma non troppo

48

Andante grazioso

*) Cadenza

Allegro ma non troppo

Printed in China

THE ART OF SCORE-READING

The first steps

A score contains the entire musical text of a musical work in order that the conductor and everyone who wants to study the piece more thoroughly can see exactly which passages are being played by the orchestra or ensemble. The parts of the individual instruments are arranged in such a way that all notes played at the same time are written one below the other.

Scores help us to listen to, understand and interpret musical works. Those who only listen to music are unaware of many important details which, after some practice, become apparent when reading the score while listening to the music. The clear structure of the score helps to easily understand the compositional style and the characteristic features of a piece – this is a prerequisite not only for any analysis but also for the musician's own performance and interpretation.

The simplest method of score-reading is to read an individual part by concentrating on an individual part that can be heard particularly well. The most suitable pieces to begin with are concertos with solo instruments such as Beethoven's Romance in F major for violin and orchestra (example 1) or orchestral songs (with them, one may easily follow the text). Furthermore, in many classical orchestral works, it is quite easy to follow the lead part of the principal violin, or the bass part in baroque compositions for orchestra.

The next step is to try to change from one part to another and vice versa and follow the part that is leading. Little by little, you learn to find distinctive parts you hear in the score as well and follow them in the corresponding staff. This can be very easily tried out with Beethoven's Symphony No. 5 (example 2). To read the score, it is also helpful to count the bars. This technique is rather useful in the case of confusing or complex scores, such as those of contemporary music, and is particularly suitable when you do not want to lag behind in any case. It should be your aim, however, to eventually give up counting the bars and to read the score by first following individual parts and then going over to section-by-section or selective reading (see next page).

Example 1 · from: Romance for violin and orchestra in F major by Beethoven

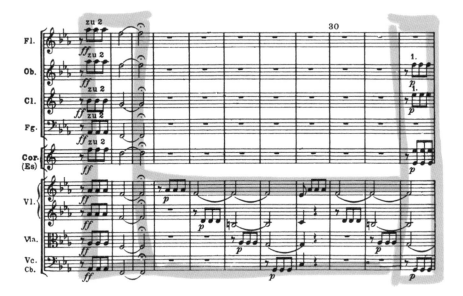

Example 2 · from: Symphony No. 5 C-minor by Beethoven

Further score-reading techniques

Example 3 · from: Symphony No. 100 G major 'Military' by Haydn

Example 4 · from: Symphony No. 41 C major 'Jupiter' by W. A. Mozart

Section-by-section reading

This technique is suitable for application in the 'Military' Symphony by Haydn (example 3). In bb. 260-264, the parts are mostly in parallel motion so that it is quite easy to take in the section as a whole. In the strings, the texture is homophonic (i.e. all instruments play the same rhythm), consisting of tone repetitions in the lower parts while there is a little more movement in the part of the first violin. At the same time, the tones of the winds are stationary (i.e. long sustained notes), serving as harmonic filling-in. If need be, they can also be read en bloc.

Such block-like structures often consist of unison figures (= all instruments play the same), such as at the beginning of Mozart's Jupiter Symphony (example 4). Here, the score-reading can first be limited to the strings section which carries the melody alone in bb. 3-4 and contains all important information.

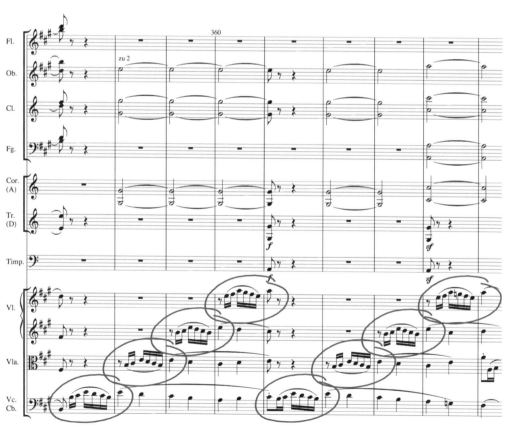

Example 5 · from: Symphony No. 7 A major by Beethoven

Selective reading

Using this technique, you concentrate on selected parts (lead parts, conspicuous passages) in the score. In the excerpt from Beethoven's Symphony No. 7 (example 5), it is the semiquaver motif that, originating with the violoncellos and basses and pervading the string parts twice, is particularly well suited. The stationary tones of the winds, consisting only of the note E in various octave positions in bb. 358-363, form the harmonic foundation and play a subordinate role in score-reading. Though they are briefly noticed, it is the strings and especially the conspicuous semiquaver motif pervading the individual parts that are to be followed.

With both score-reading techniques which should be chosen according to the nature of the passage in question, it is not important in the beginning to be able to follow at once all tones and harmonies. What matters more is to recognize and comprehend sequences of movement. Everything else comes with experience.

Following contrapuntal parts

The present excerpt from Brahms's Requiem (example 6) is polyphonic, i.e. one has to be able to follow several equal parts either alternately (without lagging behind) or simultaneously. But by looking for parallel parts in the score, the notation which, at first glance, seems to be overcrowded soon becomes clearer. For example, Brahms allocates orchestral parts to each choral part. As a consequence, there are many parts written in the score but considerably fewer independent parts actually played. Hence, the large amount of written music can be reduced to a manageable quantity.

The flute, clarinet, first violins and soprano are in parallel motion. Furthermore, the tenor of oboe and viola is supported by a much-expanded, yet parallel part. The violoncellos and bassoons too are in almost parallel motion.

The low winds and strings as well as the timpani played simultaneously with the polyphonic parts are fill-in parts which consist only of stationary tones (sustained notes). They do not need to be followed upon first reading of the score.

Seen as a whole, this excerpt is most suitable for focussing on the soprano voice as it is coupled with two instruments and, being the highest voice, can be heard very well. In addition, the text is an aid to orientation, making it easier to return from brief trips to other parts.

In fugal sections, score-reading will be easier if the entries of the theme in the score are first looked for and then marked.

Example 6 · from: A German Requiem by Brahms

The score at a glance

A **Bar lines** are solid vertical lines within the instrument sections.

B The **bar numbers** are an aid to orientation in the score. Sometimes capital letters, so-called rehearsal letters, are used instead of numbers.

C The system of parallel lines on and between which the notes are written is called **staff** (or stave). The instrument abbreviation in front of each line (here, Fl. is for 'flute') indicates to which instrument(s) the line(s) refer(s).

D The **barline at the left-hand end** of the staves connects all staves to form the **system**.

E In addition to the barline at the left-hand end of the staves, **angular brackets** connect the individual groups of instruments in a score (wind, brass and string instruments). Within these groups, the instruments are arranged according to their pitch, with the highest-pitched instrument mentioned first.
Today, the common order of instrumental parts in the score is as follows, from top to bottom:
· wind instruments
· brass instruments
· percussion instruments
· harp, piano, celesta
· solo instrument(s)
· solo voices
· choir
· string instruments

F When there are two systems on a page, they are separated from each other by two parallel **diagonal strokes**.

G Instruments the names of which are followed by 'in Bb' or (Bb) are **transposing instruments**. In this case, (Bb) indicates that the notated C is played as Bb, i.e. all tones are played a tone lower than notated. Most of the transposing instruments are easily recognizable in the score thanks to these additions. However, there are also transposing instruments without such indications in the score, such as:
· piccolo flute (in C / an octave higher)
· cor anglais (in F / a fifth lower)
· contrabassoon (in C / an octave lower)
· double bass (in C / an octave lower)

H The transposing brass instruments have no general signature but, if need be, accidentals preceding the respective tone.

I The viola part is notated in the **alto clef**, the parts of violoncello and bassoon sometimes in the **tenor clef**. Both clefs are easy to read when the player realizes that the clef frames the note C1:
alto clef   tenor clef   treble clef

J Any change of key or time is marked by a **double bar**. The alla-breve sign following in this example (¢), like the sign for four-four time (c), is a relic from an old notational practice and stands for two-two time.

63

64

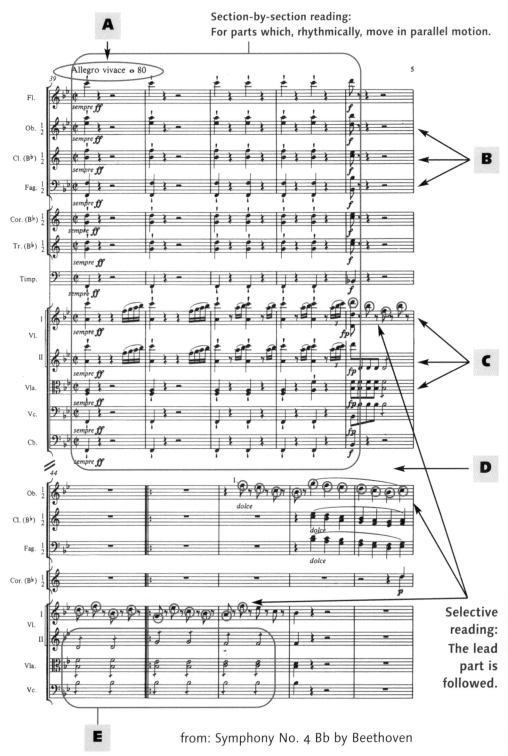

Section-by-section reading:
For parts which, rhythmically, move in parallel motion.

A

B

C

D

Selective
reading:
The lead
part is
followed.

E

from: Symphony No. 4 Bb by Beethoven

A **Tempo indications** (sometimes in connection with metronome markings) are used by the composer to indicate how fast a piece shall be played.

B In the winds, two parts are usually brought together in one line. If they play the same note, the note head either has two stems or 'a2' written above it.

C Two-part chords in the staves of the strings are played by one player. If the parts shall be divided, **divisi** (divided) is written in the score. Then, at each desk, one player plays the upper notes and another player the lower notes.

D When an instrumental part contains a long rest, as in this flute part for example, its staff is often omitted until the next entry of the instrument, thus saving space. In addition, there are less page-turns, and the playing parts are arranged much clearer.

E In order to save space and arrange phrases or groups of notes more clearly, so-called abbreviations are used occasionally. The sign ♩ stands for ♪♪♪♪, with the minim indicating the duration of the repetitions and the stroke crossing the stem indicating the value of the notes to be repeated (1 stroke = quaver, 2 strokes = semiquaver, etc.). Cf. also the viola in b. 43 in which the repeated notes are first written out and then abbreviated.

Score-Reading with pupils and students!

Order this guideline for score-reading for your class! The leaflet 'The Art of Score-Reading' is available separately or as a set of copies and can be obtained free of charge while stock last.

Brochure 'The Art of Score-Reading'
Order No. ETP 9998-99 (free of charge)

Mozart for the classroom

A picture of life and travel

Mozart was not only one of the greatest composers, but also one of the best pianists of the 18th century. Like the virtous of today, he spent a large part of his life on concert tours at the leading courts and great cities of his time.

This small brochure depicts a panorama of the musical life in Europe wich formed the background to Mozart's oeuvre. The picture is completed by a short biography and a little insight into his way of composing.

Brochure 'Mozart. A Picture of Life and Travel'
Order No. ETP 9991-99 (free of charge)

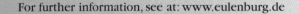

For further information, see at: www.eulenburg.de

Eulenburg

DIE KUNST
DES PARTITURLESENS

Der erste Einstieg

Eine Partitur enthält den gesamten Notentext eines Musikwerkes, damit der Dirigent und jeder, der sich näher mit dem Stück beschäftigen will, genau nachvollziehen kann, was das Orchester oder das Ensemble spielt. Dabei sind die Instrumente so angeordnet, dass alle Noten, die zur gleichen Zeit erklingen, genau untereinander stehen. Partituren helfen beim Hören, Begreifen und Interpretieren von Musikliteratur. Wer nur zuhört, erkennt viele kostbare Kleinigkeiten nicht, die beim Mitlesen nach ein wenig Übung regelrecht sichtbar werden. Der Kompositionsstil und die Charakteristik eines Werkes lassen sich mit der übersichtlichen Partitur schnell begreifen – das ist nicht nur Grundvoraussetzung für jede Analyse, sondern auch für das eigene Spiel.

Die einfachste Methode beim Partiturlesen ist das Verfolgen einer Einzelstimme. Bei diesem Verfahren konzentriert man sich auf eine einzelne Stimme, die besonders gut zu hören ist. Zum Einstieg eignen sich dabei besonders gut Konzerte mit Soloinstrumenten wie die Romanze in F-Dur für Violine und Orchester von Beethoven (Beispiel 1) oder Orchesterlieder (bei letzteren kann man sich leicht am Text orientieren). Weiterhin kann man bei vielen klassischen Orchesterwerken die führende Stimme der ersten Violine gut verfolgen, sowie bei barocken Kompositionen für Orchester die Bass-Stimme.

In einem nächsten Schritt kann man versuchen, zwischen den Stimmen zu wechseln und jeweils die Stimme zu verfolgen, die gerade führend ist. Nach und nach lernt man dabei markante Stimmen, die man hört, auch in der Partitur zu finden und im entsprechenden Notensystem zu verfolgen. Besonders anschaulich kann man das mittels Beethovens 5. Symphonie erproben (Beispiel 2).
Eine weitere Hilfe beim Lesen der Partitur kann auch das Mitzählen der Takte sein. Dieses Verfahren hilft bei unübersichtlichen oder komplexen Partituren wie etwa zeitgenössischer Musik und eignet sich besonders, wenn man den Anschluss auf keinen Fall verlieren möchte. Ziel sollte es jedoch sein, das Mitzählen der Takte gänzlich zu verlassen und die Partitur zunächst anhand einzelner Stimmen und dann im Wechsel von blockweisem bzw. selektivem Lesen zu verfolgen (siehe nächste Seite).

Beispiel 1 · aus: Romanze für Violine und Orchester F-Dur von Beethoven

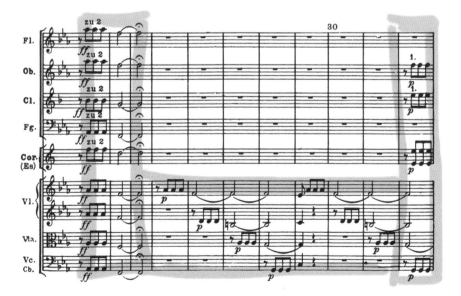

Beispiel 2 · aus: Symphonie Nr. 5 c-moll von Beethoven

Weitere Methoden des Partiturlesens

Beispiel 3 · aus: Symphonie Nr. 100 G-Dur „Militär" von Haydn

Beispiel 4 · aus: Symphonie Nr. 41 C-Dur „Jupiter" von W. A. Mozart

Blockweises Lesen

Diese Methode bietet sich in der Militär-Symphonie von Haydn an (Beispiel 3). In den T. 260-264 sind die Stimmen weitgehend parallel geführt, so dass man sie gut im Ganzen überblicken kann. In den Streichern haben wir einen homophonen Satz (d.h. alle Stimmen spielen den gleichen Rhythmus), der in den unteren Stimmen aus Tonwiederholungen besteht, während die erste Violine etwas bewegter ist. Gleichzeitig erklingen in den Bläserstimmen Liegetöne (d.h. lang ausgehaltene Töne), die als harmonischer Füllstoff dienen. Sie können bei Bedarf auch im Block gelesen werden.

Oft bestehen solche blockhaften Gebilde auch aus unisono-Figuren (= alle Stimmen spielen dasselbe), wie z.B. am Beginn der Jupiter-Symphonie von Mozart (Beispiel 4). Hier kann man sich beim Lesen zunächst nur auf den Streicherblock beschränken, der in den T. 3-4 alleine die Melodie weiterführt und bereits alle wichtigen Informationen enthält.

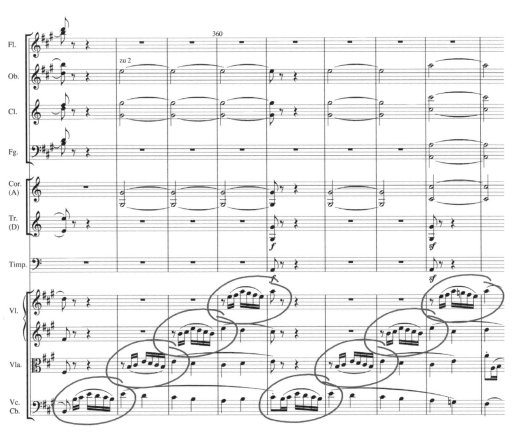

Beispiel 5 · aus: Symphonie Nr. 7 A-Dur von Beethoven

Selektives Lesen

Bei dieser Methode orientiert man sich anhand ausgewählter Stimmen (führende Stimmen, auffällige Stellen) in der Partitur. Im Ausschnitt aus Beethovens 7. Symphonie (Beispiel 5) ist hierzu das Sechzehntelmotiv geeignet, das zweimal von den Celli und Bässen ausgehend durch die Streicherstimmen wandert. Die Liegetöne der Bläser, die in den T. 358-363 sogar nur aus dem Ton e in unterschiedlichen Oktavlagen bestehen, bilden die harmonische Grundierung und spielen beim Lesen der Partitur eine untergeordnete Rolle. Man nimmt sie kurz wahr, verfolgt jedoch die Streicher und dort insbesondere das auffällige Sechzehntelmotiv in seiner Wanderung durch die einzelnen Stimmen.
Bei beiden Leseformen, zwischen denen man übrigens je nach Beschaffenheit der Stelle wechseln sollte, kommt es am Anfang nicht darauf an, sofort alle Töne und Harmonien verfolgen zu können. Viel wichtiger ist es, Bewegungsabläufe zu erkennen und nachzuvollziehen. Alles Weitere kommt mit der Erfahrung.

Verfolgen von kontrapunktischen Stimmen

Der vorliegende Ausschnitt aus Brahms' Requiem (Beispiel 6) ist polyphon komponiert, d.h. man muss mehrere gleichwertige Stimmen entweder im Wechsel (ohne den Anschluss zu verlieren) oder gleichzeitig verfolgen können.
Doch das auf den ersten Blick so übervolle Notenbild lichtet sich bald, wenn man sich die Partitur näher auf parallele Stimmen ansieht. Brahms ordnet z.B. jeder Chorstimme Orchesterstimmen zu. Das hat zur Folge, dass hier zwar viele Stimmen notiert sind, aber wesentlich weniger eigenständige Stimmen tatsächlich erklingen. Die vielen geschriebenen Noten lassen sich also auf ein überschaubares Maß reduzieren.
So werden Flöte, Klarinette, erste Violinen und Sopran parallel geführt. Des Weiteren wird der Tenor von Oboe und Bratsche mit einer stark erweiterten, aber dennoch parallel verlaufenden Stimme unterstützt. Ebenfalls fast ganz parallel verlaufen Violoncelli und Fagotte.
Zu den polyphon gefügten Stimmen erklingen die tiefen Bläser und Streicher sowie die Pauke mit Füllstimmen, welche lediglich aus Liegetönen (ausgehaltene Töne) bestehen. Sie braucht man beim ersten Lesen nicht weiter zu verfolgen.
Im Ganzen gesehen bietet sich in diesem Ausschnitt an, schwerpunktmäßig die Sopranstimme zu verfolgen, da sie mit zwei Instrumenten gekoppelt ist und als höchste Stimme gut herauszuhören ist. Zudem bietet der Text eine Orientierungshilfe, so dass der Wiedereinstieg von vorübergehenden Ausflügen in andere Stimmen erleichtert wird.
Bei fugierten Abschnitten kann man sich das Mitlesen auch erleichtern, indem man zunächst alle Einsätze des Themas in der Partitur sucht und sich markiert.

Beispiel 6 · aus: Ein deutsches Requiem von Brahms

Die Partitur im Überblick

A **Taktstriche** sind innerhalb der Instrumentengruppen durchgezogen.

B Die **Taktzahlen** erleichtern die Orientierung in der Partitur. Manchmal dienen hierzu auch Großbuchstaben, sog. Studierbuchstaben.

C Eine einzelne Zeile der Partitur nennt man **Notensystem**. Für welche(s) Instrument(e) sie steht, zeigt der **Instrumentenvorsatz** an (hier Fl. für Flöte).

D Der **Kopfstrich** verbindet alle Notensysteme miteinander zu einer **Akkolade**.

E Zusätzlich zum Kopfstrich fassen **gerade Klammern** die einzelnen Instrumentengruppen (Holz-, Blech- und Streichinstrumente) zusammen. Innerhalb dieser Gruppen sind die Instrumente nach Tonlage geordnet, wobei das höchste an oberster Stelle steht.
Die heute übliche Partituranordnung lautet von oben nach unten:
· Holzblasinstrumente
· Blechblasinstrumente
· Schlaginstrumente
· Harfe, Klavier, Celesta
· Soloinstrument(e)
· Solostimmen
· Chor
· Streichinstrumente

F Stehen zwei Akkoladen auf einer Seite, werden sie durch zwei **Schrägstriche** voneinander abgetrennt.

G Steht hinter dem Instrumentennamen z.B. „in B" oder (B), handelt es sich um ein **transponierendes Instrument**. In diesem Fall deutet das (B) an, dass das notierte C als B erklingt, also alle Noten einen Ton tiefer erklingen als sie notiert sind. Die meisten transponierenden Instrumente sind in der Partitur durch diese Zusätze leicht zu erkennen. Es gibt aber auch transponierende Instrumente ohne eine entsprechende Angabe in der Partitur, wie z.B.:
Piccoloflöte (in c/eine Oktave höher)
Englischhorn (in f/eine Quinte tiefer)
Kontrafagott (in c/eine Oktave tiefer)
Kontrabass (in c/eine Oktave tiefer)

H Die transponierenden Blechblasinstrumente haben keine Generalvorzeichen, sondern bei Bedarf Versetzungszeichen, die direkt vor der jeweiligen Note stehen.

I Die Viola oder Bratsche wird im **Alt- bzw. Bratschenschlüssel** notiert, die Stimmen des Violoncellos und Fagotts manchmal im **Tenorschlüssel**. Beide Schlüssel sind leicht zu lesen, wenn man sich klarmacht, dass der Schlüssel den Ton c1 umrahmt, also:
Alt-   Tenor-   Violinschlüssel

J Vor einem Wechsel der Ton- oder Taktart steht immer ein **Doppelstrich**. Das hier folgende Alla-Breve-Zeichen (¢) ist ebenso wie das Zeichen für den 4/4-Takt (c) ein Relikt aus einer älteren Notationspraxis und steht für den 2/2-Takt.

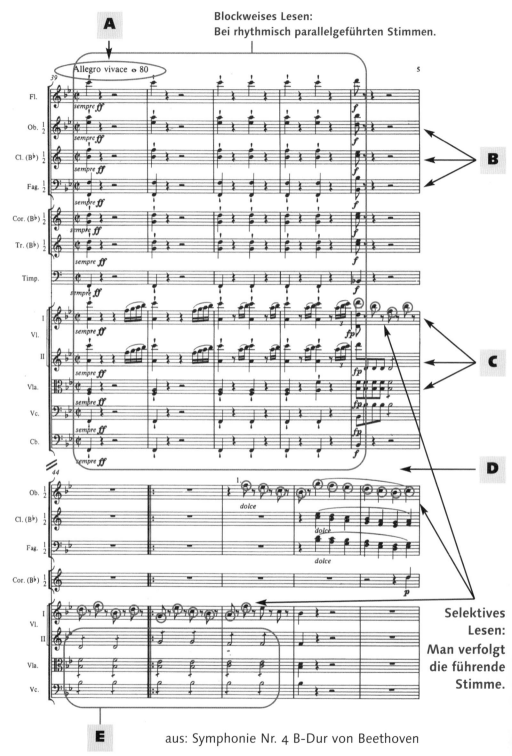

aus: Symphonie Nr. 4 B-Dur von Beethoven

A Durch die **Tempoangabe** (manchmal mit einer Metronomzahl verbunden) gibt der Komponist an, wie schnell ein Stück gespielt werden soll.

B Bei den Bläsern werden in der Regel zwei Stimmen in einer Notenzeile zusammengefasst. Spielen sie den gleichen Ton, erhält der Notenkopf zwei Hälse oder es steht a2 darüber.

C Zweistimmige Akkorde in den Notensystemen der Streicher werden von einem Spieler gespielt. Will man die Stimmen aufteilen, schreibt man **divisi** (geteilt). Dann spielt an jedem Pult ein Spieler die oberen und ein Spieler die unteren Noten.

D Hat eine Stimme, wie hier die Flöte, längere Zeit Pause, wird ihr Notensystem oft bis zum erneuten Einsatz der Stimme weggelassen. So wird Platz gespart, man muß weniger blättern und die erklingenden Stimmen sind übersichtlicher angeordnet.

E Um Platz zu sparen und Tonfolgen übersichtlicher zu gestalten, verwendet man gelegentlich sogenannte **Abbreviaturen (Faulenzer)**. Das hier verwendete Zeichen ♩ steht für ♪♪♪♪, wobei die Halbe Note die Dauer der Wiederholungen anzeigt und der Strich durch den Notenhals den Wert der zu wiederholenden Noten (1 Strich = Achtel, 2 = Sechzehntel usw.). Vgl. auch die Viola in T. 43, in der zunächst die Repetitionen ausgeschrieben und dann abgekürzt sind.

Partiturlesen im Klassensatz

Diese kurze Einführung können Sie als kostenloses Faltblatt bestellen – gern auch im Klassensatz!

Faltblatt "Die Kunst des Partiturlesens"
Bestellnummer: ETP 9999-99 (kostenlos)

Die passende Ergänzung für Klassen- und Unterrichtsräume:

Plakat A2 "Die Partitur im Überblick"
Bestellnummer ETP 9950-99 (kostenlos)

Mozart im Klassensatz

Ein Lebens- und Reisebild
Mozart war nicht nur einer der größten Komponisten, sondern auch einer der besten Pianisten des 18. Jahrhunderts. Wie heutige Virtuosen verbrachte er große Teile seines Lebens auf Konzertreisen zwischen den führenden Höfen und großen Städten seiner Zeit. Diese kleine Broschüre entfaltet ein Panorama des europäischen Musiklebens, das den Hintergrund für Mozarts Schaffen bildete. Eine Kurzbiographie und ein kleiner Einblick in seine Schreibweise runden das Bild ab.

Faltblatt "Mozart. Ein Lebens- und Reisebild"
Bestellnummer ETP 9990-99 (kostenlos)

Weitere Informationen unter www.eulenburg.de

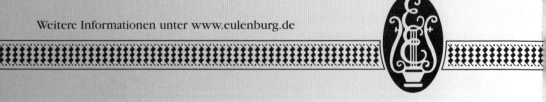

Eulenburg